Pick it up

Speed Sounds

Consonants   *Ask children to say the sounds.*

f	l	m	n	r	s	v	z	sh	**th**	**ng**
					ss					**nk**

b	c	d	g	h	j	p	qu	t	w	x	y	**ch**
	k											
	ck											

Vowels   *Ask children to say the sounds in and out of order.*

a	e	i	o	u

*Each box contains one sound but sometimes
more than one grapheme.
Focus graphemes for this story are **circled**.*

Ditty 1 Pick it up

Story Green Words

Ask children to read the words first in Fred Talk and then say the word.

pick   that   sock   vest

mess

Pick it up

pick up that sock

yes

pick up that vest

yes

pick up that mess

Story Green Words

Ask children to read the words first in Fred Talk and then say the word.

six   pink   red

long   snap

Ask children to read the root first and then the whole word with the suffix.

rat → rats   hat → hats   croc → crocs

sock → socks

Snap snap

Introduction

This is a story about some rats and some crocodiles.
The rats are a bit worried... can you guess why?

six pink rats in big red hats

six red crocs in long pink socks

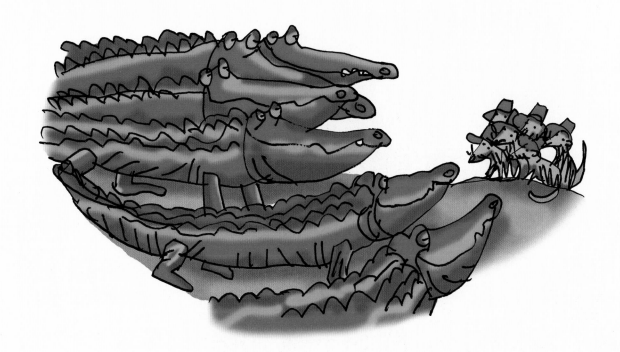

snap snap snap

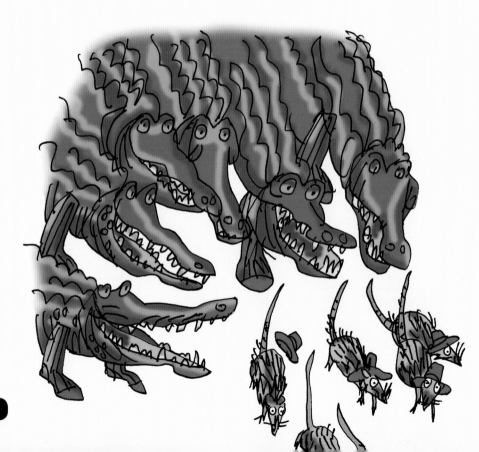

Ditty 3 This chimp can run

Story Green Words

Ask children to read the words first in Fred Talk and then say the word.

this	chimp	run	grin
clap	that	win	

This chimp can run

Introduction

*When you play a game, do you like to win? This is
a story about some chimps who are at a sports day.
Let's see what they do!*

this chimp can run

that chimp can grin

this chimp can clap

that chimp can win

Questions to talk about

*Read out each question and ask children to TTYP (turn to your partner)
and discuss.*

Ditty 1

What does the boy pick up first?

What does the boy say to his mum at the end of the story?

What does your mum/dad/carer ask you to pick up off your bedroom floor?

Ditty 2

How many rats are there?

What are the crocs wearing?

What sort of things do you like dressing up in?

Ditty 3

What can the first chimp do?

What three things can the other chimps do?

Why is this chimp so clever?

Speedy Green Words

*Ask children to practise reading the words across the rows, down
the columns and in and out of order clearly and quickly.*

up	yes	in	big
can	up	yes	can